Nicole

Tooty's Corner

Michael Maione

*From my corner
to yours*

*Michael Maione
(The Miley)*

Tooty's Corner
Michael Maione

Pentland Press, Inc.
England • USA • Scotland

"Tooty's checks out" by Jim Ritter, Staff Reporter, from the July 6, 1998 issue of the *Chicago Sun-Times* was reprinted with permission, *The Chicago Sun-Times* © 1998

PUBLISHED BY PENTLAND PRESS, INC.
5122 Bur Oak Circle, Raleigh, North Carolina 27612
United States of America
919-782-0281

ISBN 1-57197-131-9
Library of Congress Catalog Card Number 98-067425

Printed in the United States of America

"One good thing about being young is that you are not experienced enough to know you cannot possibly do the things you are doing."

Special thanks to Julie Bennett for her editorial assistance.

This story is dedicated to the guys from Tooty's Corner, 1955.

Charlie Bolts	Fat Frankie*	Richie Cat
The Miles	Norman Bates	Joe Boz
Nick the Stick	The Molly	Tony Boy
The Professor	Petey Boy	Yo Yo
Bobbie D*	The Chain	Richie Rags
Ollie	Johnny Boy	Kenny
Naps	Mikey	Lory*
Sonny	Butchie	Skinny Green*
Jimmy Boy	Tooty (The Man)	The Meyers

*Denotes morte

Contents

The Beginning

"How many years has it been since all of us from the corner have gotten together?" bellowed Yo-Yo while scoffing down a gigantic beef sandwich on the afternoon of 25 June 1994.

"What the hell brought that on?" I asked. "Don't you like the present time frame?"

"Shit, let's talk thirty-five years or longer," said Richie Rags who, with me, the Miles, was bullshitting about the past as we normally do when the three of us get together for lunch at the local Italian deli in the old neighborhood.

"Have you seen Charlie Bolts?" I asked.

"About fifteen years ago," answered Rags. "Someone said he was not feeling good lately."

"Bullshit! I can't believe that," I said. "I cannot imagine Bolts not being strong. He's not the type." I was always positive about Bolts. Bolts had been my boyhood idol even though there was only a three year age difference between us. Charlie Bolts was the super jock of the fifties. Bolts went to St. Rita High School and so did I. Bolts was an excellent basketball player and so was I. Whatever Bolts did, I did.

"What about Skinny Green?" asked Yo-Yo.

"Morte Skinny Green," I said. "Morte" meaning dead.

"Has anyone seen Butchie?" Yo-Yo asked. "He's a big shot these days. I don't think he wants to come back to the neighborhood anymore."

"That's bullshit," said Rags, "He'll come."

The conversation went back and forth between the three of us until Rags asked, "Do you really want to see everyone again or should we keep the mystique of the corner in our minds?" Deep down Rags was the biggest advocate of getting everyone together. Talk of a reunion made him excited and he wanted it to take place anytime, anywhere.

I said, "Trying to find everyone will be a gigantic pain in the ass, but I'm game if both of you will help out. Just maybe with all of us together we can pull it off."

> "Do you really want to see everyone again or should we keep the mystique of the corner in our minds?"

Yo-Yo chimed in, "Yeah, Miles, let's do it."

"Let's meet back here next week. Be sure you have a list of guys together. It should only be open to the first guys on the corner in 1955, and not everyone who came and went after that. Otherwise, we'll have a nightmare on our hands and a hundred guys will want to come."

Rags said, "We'll piss off a lot of the guys if we don't open it to everyone. Besides that, it's 1994. Who the fuck cares who was first or last? Let's just go and have a good time."

"Fuck them. Let 'em be pissed. Just the first twenty or so guys," I said. "We were the original guys—the first—and that's important. Let's keep it simple. Besides that, what would they be pissed off about anyway?"

"Okay, okay," said Yo-Yo and Rags together. Although they didn't agree, they went along anyway at my insistence.

"Everyone compile a list so we'll be in agreement," I said.

As the conversation shifted, we knew something from our past was about to be reborn and that it was worth getting excited about.

Rags had stayed close with some of the guys that were not on the invite list and he caught a lot of shit when they found out they were being left off. Guys came and went the first two years that the corner was in its heyday.

Several meetings later, we were riding on a cloud of anticipation since, after talking with some of the guys, we had received favorable responses to the idea of a reunion. Rags said he was getting a lot of opposition from guys that weren't invited. I again said, with a louder and more determined voice of disapproval, "No fuckin' way. You guys are buckling under the pressure. Pretty soon you'll want to bring the women and really fuck this thing up."

"No, no!" Yo-Yo shouted. "I won't come either. No broads! They didn't hang on the corner anyway. Why should they be part of it now?"

"Attaboy, Yo-Yo! That's balls," I said. My mind was made up regardless of any opposition I might encounter.

I was the only one who brought an invite list, but the other two agreed that it was complete. Some guys lived out of state, like the Professor who was in Virginia, Johnny Boy in Louisiana, Ollie and Kenny were last seen in California, and Mikey in Lake Tahoe.

"Let's find out who has the phone numbers so we can get started." Rags remembered that Nick the Stick was an insurance agent and that he might have phone numbers of some of the guys from having done business with them. We figured we could also find phone numbers by asking the families that were still in the neighborhood. Most of the guys were in and around Chicago, so they would probably be easy to locate. We decided to split the list and start making calls.

Pretty soon it was evident there would be a good turnout. I located Johnny Boy in Louisiana, but was told that he and his family would be on vacation in Sweden until after the reunion. However, the following morning in my office, I got a phone call from Johnny Boy who said, "Hey, Miles, fuck Sweden! How many times am I going to see the corner guys in my life again? I'll cut the trip short. Get me a room at your hotel and count me in."

"That's great," I bellowed. I called Rags and Yo-Yo to tell them the news.

The only negative phone call came from the Junk Man who told Yo-Yo he wasn't interested in seeing anyone or in returning to the corner for any reunion. Rags hit the nail on the head when he said, "Why are you surprised? Junk Man was an asshole in '55. What makes you think he'd be changed by now?"

Naps was excited about the phone call inviting him to the dinner and remarked, "This will be something that's positive. I'm used to going to funerals where you see people in the box and you can't talk to them. This way, I can see and talk to everyone again. I can't wait."

As they were all called one by one, it was decided to have a reception and dinner on 26 August at the Doubletree Hotel where I worked. Yo-Yo insisted that the wait staff wear fifties clothing and play music from the performers of the period like the Gaylords, Four Aces, and Fats Domino or maybe bring one of those groups in to perform live. I joked, pointing to the sky, "They are all probably dead now and singing up there."

All the plans were in place. We walked to our cars and went our separate ways until we met again at the reunion.

First Time In Thirty-Nine Years

Yo-Yo hung a sign on the front of Tooty's building facing Princeton Avenue. It proudly read, "Welcome Back The Guys 1955." The sign was proof that everything was taking shape despite all the rumblings about who was and was not invited.

The excitement built all day and neither Yo-Yo, Rags, nor I could get any work done.

"Did you see Johnny Boy?" Rags asked me. "He was supposed to check in today at the hotel."

"No I didn't, but I'm sure we will see him. Let's wait till around 4:00 P.M. and check then. Don't worry. He'll come and so will the others."

I drove to the corner at 5:45 P.M. to find almost everyone milling around, talking, and hugging one

> *"It was truly like the old days, especially when Charlie Bolts handled the pitch of Joe Boz by lifting a soft pop-up over the fence of Old Man Scalise's yard, which had the same look as it did in the fifties and played out just like it was supposed to."*

another. Someone yelled, "Hey, there's Naps!" Naps showed up in a brand new $450.00 suit. "I know I'm a good looking guy and in great shape," Naps commented, "but why am I the only one dressed in a suit?"

Everyone was there except Richie Cat and he actually lived the closest to the corner. The arrangement was for everyone to meet on the corner by 6:00 P.M., just like we had done the summer of 1955. Deep down I knew the Cat would not show up until around 6:20 P.M. or even 6:30 P.M. Captain Video came on at 6:00 P.M. each evening, Monday through Friday. Cat and I were faithful watchers and it was only on for fifteen minutes. Only after this program was over did the Cat come to the corner. Sure enough, the Cat being the last to arrive with his handkerchief in hand was greeted with, "Where the hell have you been, it's almost time to leave?" The Cat responded, "My man, Captain Video, was on and I don't leave my house until he's over. But I made it."

"Yeah, so you did," chimed in Ollie who, with tears in his eyes, greeted everyone with a handshake and a hug.

The gathering on the corner
1994

About fifty onlookers watched—sisters, brothers, kids, and the few mothers and fathers who were still alive—and greeted everyone. "Joey you look good!" exclaimed Molly's mother who enjoyed watching the reunion. She and her husband owned a tavern in the middle of the block on Princeton Avenue, down the street from Tooty's. She made sure that Molly brought her to the corner that night. They made some great sandwiches in that tavern. All of the guys could still hear her saying to us as kids, "Food okay, booze not okay."

It truly was like the old days, especially when Charlie Bolts handled the pitch of Joe Boz by lifting a soft pop-up over the fence of Old Man Scalise's yard, which had the same look as it did in the fifties and played out just like it was supposed to. The ball, you see, never came back and we didn't expect it to. Only years later did I find out that the balls sent over the fence while we played four corners were given to the grandson of the old man, Joe Bonomo, who just happens to be my good friend of today. It's amazing that Old Man Scalise lived as long as he did, considering all the guys wished him dead every time he kept a ball during a hot summer game.

We popped the champagne and toasted the corner, Tooty, and all the guys dead and alive. We posed for pictures which, without us knowing at the time, would show up on the front page of the *Chicago Sun Times* the following morning. The local television show also did a tribute to the corner and the reunion on the following Monday. We proceeded to our cars so we could enjoy the moment and the memories.

Let's Get Back To The Stories

As I looked over the group of guys on the corner for the first time in thirty-nine years and saw what time had done to us all, both good and bad, I could only remember . . .

Boy, it was a hot day. It must have been 110 degrees in the shade. It was a typical late summer morning only because I slept until 10:00 A.M., as I always did in the summertime. You see, I was the only son in the household. This meant, much to the dismay of my sister, Rosemary, that I was exempt from chores because in most Italian households the sons and fathers were the kings. And quite frankly, I didn't see why my household would or should be any different.

I didn't have anything to do except hang out, play a little ball, and basically just rest and relax. And to think I got away with it. As I walked through the gangway on Princeton Avenue between the Passie's house who lived next to us and my house, my mind wandered out loud to my imagined story. ". . . The score is four to four, bases loaded, score tied last of the ninth and Mike Maione is at the plate. Billy Pierce lays a fastball down the middle and Maione swings. Holy cow! He whacked that ball and it's going . . . going . . . gone!"

This story was played out in my mind almost every morning in the gangway because I wanted it to be true someday. The reverberation off the building walls sounded like I was in a tunnel (furnishing great sound effects). As I finished rounding the bases (because I always hit that home run in my mind), I glanced and saw Fat Frankie doing his usual thing when it was hot—not moving and sitting on the stoop. Fat Frankie fit his name. He weighed around two hundred eighty pounds. Not bad for a kid sixteen years old, or should I say not good? His weight eventually took its toll many years later, but then that's another story.

"Hey Fats, let's take a walk to the park, pick up a few guys on the way, and spend the rest of the day playing some ball."

"Miles, Miles, please, it's too hot. Besides it's almost noon and I am sorta hungry," which meant that Frankie was extremely hungry. "Let's stop at Tooty's and have him make us a jalung sandwich. We'll split it and spend the next

> *This story was played out in my mind almost every morning in the gangway, because I wanted it to be true someday.*

hour or so enjoying ourselves. And I know you have a few dinero in your pocket, so you buy this time, and I'll get the next."

Fat Frankie was right about that and he knew that I was a sucker for a jalung sandwich. But let me first explain the famous jalung sandwich. It's very simple—one loaf of Italian bread split down the side, two pounds of assorted meats like capacole and salami, with tomatoes and lettuce, and cut in half. With a bottle of pop, it made for an enjoyable hour or so of eating pleasure, a real food orgy that made the afternoon.

Food brought guys to the corner and this day was no different as Fats and I talked over the upcoming day's events. All of a sudden, we heard a loud, high voice that could only be coming from Skinny Green. Why the name Skinny Green? He was extremely skinny and he always dressed himself in green—socks, shirt, hat. Many of the guys thought his ass was green but luckily we never found out, nor did we want to. "Save me some of the sandwich you guys."

"Fuck you," we retorted, "go buy your own." That was the usual ritual of words when someone wanted something and that person refused.

"Never mind food. Go find us a bat and ball and we'll walk to the park," which was around six blocks away. "We'll get a game together."

"C'mon you got to be good for something," these words came from Charlie Bolts, our corner hotshot. Bolts had all the athletic ability in the world. But then he was three years older, so he pretty much beat the shit out of everyone, especially when he played one-on-one basketball in the alley. Almost all I learned about basketball I learned from Charlie Bolts in the alley around the corner from Tooty's.

When I played high school and college ball, my memories always drifted back to the alley. One-on-one with Charlie Bolts was a great learning experience for me and I didn't even know it at the time. I did thank him one last time at the reunion. Charlie never played organized ball although he always excelled. Often he was too busy making money after school, working deals, and doing other shit. Had he actually tried he would have been a damn good player.

We never made it to the park that day and we very seldom went except on weekends unless we had a money game going. You see, the corner became a meeting place everyday, early in the morning and late at night. Tooty never kicked us off and no one really knows why to this day. Why would anyone want twenty-five or thirty guys standing around playing cards, dice, or four-corner baseball every day? We never were loud, or so we thought. Then again, who would mess with Tooty with all those guys standing around seven days a week? Tooty lived upstairs from the store and still does to this day.

The corner eventually became our space. We were choosy regarding who came and went. Playing fast pitching, eating jalung sandwiches, pitching pennies, sitting around doing nothing, and using the corner as a starting point to a show or ballgame became the way of life for us that summer and what a summer it was.

The Corner Executive Committee

In many ways, we operated the corner like a major corporation. We had our executive committee which consisted of Charlie Bolts, Lory, Fat Frankie, Richie Cat, and Richie Rags. We also had our senior managers and our middle level people. Everyone wanted to be accepted by our executive committee, which meant going for jalung sandwiches, chasing balls, getting change, and generally laughing at everything the so-called committee said—even at Fat Frankie's stupid jokes. Charlie Bolts was older, stronger than most, super athletic, and always had money. He got respect for that. Then there was Lory. Who would want to mess with him? If you did, you'd walk around with your face split, so you showed respect. Pounding heads was his favorite pastime. I didn't mind that as long as it wasn't my head he was pounding. He was protection if you needed it. Fat Frankie was always good at telling stories. He kept everyone in a pretty good mood and, surprisingly, he was good with the broads. They liked his sense of humor and he was fat and safe. Speaking of being good with the broads, Richie Rags and Richie Cat were the best. Broads flocked to them. Cat had the personality and Rags had the looks—together they made a good team and that was our executive committee.

Our senior level guys were the athletics like Nick the Stick, Bobbie D., Norman Bates, Petey Boy, Joe Boz, Sonny, and me. Our middle level people consisted of Yo-Yo, Ollie, Naps, the Molly, the Chain, Mikey, and Tony Boy. Most were popular and had money. Our lower level people had none of the above attributes, but they were only there for short periods of time. They were Johnny Boy, Butchie, Kenny, Skinny Green, the Professor, and of course, the Meyers. We used to call these guys to fill in or be part of the scenery. They were there, but at the same time they weren't. They didn't participate in any sports, chase girls, play cards or dice, or get into any fights. In fact, they were like the post on the corner. But they were

> "Cat had the personality and Rags had the looks—together they made a good team and that was our executive committee."

stand-up guys that certainly played an integral part of the corner in some indescribable way.

Baseball For Big Dollars

On the corner one Friday, Petey came with a request. "My cousin thinks he has quite a baseball club and they want to play a money game with us some Sunday afternoon in their park on the far south side." We were known as the south side. If you lived south of 63rd Street, you would be considered the far south side. They would not come to our neighborhood because, for some reason, and God only knows where they got this from, they thought if they won they would never get out of the park with the money.

Of course, we all said, "Bullshit, that's no reason for not wanting to come down here to play. What assholes!" Nevertheless, when money was on the line, the guys responded favorably.

"Let's do this right away," exclaimed Richie Cat. "I could use the bread. Petey, get them to play next Sunday." Petey did; he set it up for $25.00 per man with a start time of 4:00 P.M. This was a lot of money for most of us and Charlie Bolts again came to the rescue. He put the money up for anyone not having it and if we won he would take his usual ten percent commission. If we lost, God forbid, Charlie said he would take it out of our asses.

After driving all the way to the far south side, we arrived at this so-called ball field (it turned out to be a school yard with a short left field wall). Petey's cousin's team had the latest uniforms and even had baseball shoes. We were lucky to have shoes,

> "Nevertheless, when money was on the line, the guys responded favorably."

let alone baseball shoes. Despite this, we all knew when Cat hit the first pitch on top of the wall that the other team was in deep shit. Nick the Stick suggested that we all bat left-handed since, if we truly played legit, this game would be over in two innings. We all knew we could hit the wall at any time by batting right-handed, so we toyed with them for nine innings.

We only won by three runs, thanks to a line drive between left and center by Sonny. After Petey's cousin, who was pissed, talked with his team, they decided they wanted to play another game for more money. Charlie Bolts had an orgasm. Man he loved sitting there counting his money. Charlie suggested $50.00 per man and they agreed.

"What big assholes," said Tony Boy.

"I second the motion," Naps said as he was counting his side bets—a cool $70.00. At $50.00 per man, we had to teach them not to fuck with Tooty's guys.

We all batted right-handed and scored twenty-two runs in the first two innings. They quit because they knew it would only get worse. "Pizza for everyone," yelled Charlie Bolts as we jumped into the cars for the trip home. I don't think Petey talked to his cousin for a whole year. Word spread quickly that we screwed some guys from the far south side in a baseball game so it was difficult to find some soft touches again, especially in other parts of the city.

Richie Rags And His Girl Ro

Rags was the guy who always looked like a million dollars. His old man was a barber so his hair was always neat and in style. He also had plenty of it to show. Rags was often called the pretty boy of the corner. His clothes were never out of place and he never sweat no matter what he did. We used to kid him about getting dirty, which was something he also never did. Even when he was playing ball or washing his father's car, he always looked good. Rags, like Lory, always had broads chasing him and everybody liked to spend evenings with him because of the possibility of ending up in the back seat of a car. Rags was one of the best. Why hang with the Meyers or Butchie and end up with the *Tribune*, when you could go with Rags and come home with wet pants and sore lips?

All this, of course, was prior to Ro. Rags was the only guy on the corner to go steady. I guess Ro stole his heart, but then again Ro could have stolen many hearts in those

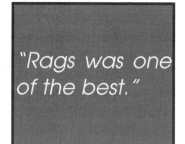

"Rags was one of the best."

days. She rated a perfect high number with personality to boot. Most nights were spent in two places for Rags, on the steps in front of Ro's house on Wells Street or on the corner. When Ro had to go in for something, Rags would run over to the corner to see what was happening and of course received all kinds of shit from whoever was there at the time. "Hey Rags when are you going to spend more than five minutes on the corner with us?" or "You pussy, stick around and hang with the guys!" Rags would just look at whoever was giving him the shit and walk back to Ro's house. Those two eventually got married and are still married to this day. It must be forty years, but to Rags and his girl Ro it probably only seems like ten.

Richie Rags and Ro

Bolts, Bobby D., And The Professor

DAs, box toe shoes, suede shoes, peg pants, and the Chicago Cardinals. What combinations! Suede shoes, peg pants, and fans of the Cardinals were our favorite things for a short period of time, but the DA was totally out of the question. A DA was a hairstyle shaped in the way a duck's ass parts down the middle with your hair reaching out to the part. The Professor found out the DA was forbidden when one day he showed his new hairstyle to the group of us sitting around. Unfortunately for the Professor, Bolts was also there and he did not take to DAs. He said, "That's west side Eddie hair." Nobody ever asked Bolts what that meant. It was a strange statement and what's even stranger is that it actually worked. We all stood around and said, "Yeah, west side

Eddie hair." Bolts gave the Professor a whack on the head and told him to get a comb and work it out, and not to come back until his hair was normal. Another strange statement. Until your hair is normal? I saw Butchie sitting on the stoop and I know what he was thinking, "What the fuck does he mean 'normal'?"

The Professor looked good with that cut because he had a lot of hair to move around. But he did as he was told and became part of the group again. He was also afraid of wearing peg pants for fear of Bolts giving him a whack in the balls, so he decided to stay away from all the fads for the time being.

> "Bolts gave the Professor a whack on the head and told him to get a comb and work it out, and not to come back until his hair was normal. Another strange statement."

The Chicago Cardinals, Chicago's other professional football team, played at Comiskey Park during those days and it was great fun to watch them practice after school. We could go down to the Park and get in for free, as a lot of guys did. The Cardinals had their dream backfield and we thought we had ours. We never played tackle football. We played touch instead, mainly because we could not afford all the equipment that goes along with tackle, like helmets, shoulder pads, et cetera, and we had to walk a mile to the park to play on a grass field. There was no grass on the corner and none at Spatts Field either. So, we were forced into the streets, dodging cars and dogs and going after the long bomb thrown by Bobbie D., our local high school quarterback. Bobbie D. was a good touch football player and he was the starting quarterback for Tilden Tech High School's football team, which never won a game with Bobby D. as quarterback. But who cared? We had him throwing balls for us on the corner. We played some of the greatest touch football games ever between 28th and 29th Streets in the old neighborhood.

Molly And Norman's Last Ride

Norman Bates and the Molly were the resident Croatian guys or "Modges" as we called them along with the Boz and Nick the Stick. They shared the corner with two Germans and twenty-five Italians. However, Norman and Molly had one other thing in common. They had a motorbike, motor scooter, or a board with a motor on it. Whatever you wanted to call it, it worked. They would run on $1.00 worth of gas for the month and through rain, snow, sleet, or anything else that happened to be on the streets of Chicago that month. Of course, you could only take one person with you on the bike, so needless to say, they were quite popular. When you wanted to go somewhere fast, Bates and Norman would offer to take you for a small fee. Molly was extremely busy whenever he needed money and would cover a five mile radius of the corner. Just catch Norman or Molly coming down Princeton Avenue, pay the fee, and away you went.

Molly undercut Norman on the price so he was much busier most of the time.

"How much Molly?" we'd ask.

"Ten cents a block . . . six blocks back and forth . . . that's $1.20 round trip."

We'd say, "But I don't want to come back."

He'd retort, "Fuck you! I have to, so you have to pay both ways."

Molly was always thinking ahead. He made around $10.00 per day. Molly was never much into sports. He was more of a money guy or a con artist, as we called him, especially when he was charging us those rates. But I must admit, he saved you a lot of time.

"He was more of a money guy or a con artist, as we called him, especially when he was charging us those rates."

One winter day, the streets were full of ice and snow which usually meant Molly did not take the scooter out. However, this day was different. He was getting through the slop pretty clean and fast. Just when things were going good, the bike slipped out from under him and Molly landed on his head next to a concrete stoop while the bike went around a post.

Nobody knew who was in worse shape, the bike or Molly. Molly went to the hospital and the bike went to the junkyard. Molly's father aptly put it, "That's it! That's it! No more bike, you walk like everyone else." Molly recovered, but the bike did not. Bates' father followed suit. No more bike for him either. Norman did not like that at all. Bates went to visit Molly in the hospital and informed him what a big asshole he was for fucking up his motor scooter days.

The following summer, Bates and Molly had cars to run up and down the neighborhood instead. Coincidentally, Bates was the first to fuck up his car with an accident on 31st Street. Molly didn't say anything to Norman, but we knew what he was thinking when he found out what happened. At least there was no old man around to take his car away.

Tony Boy And His Cast Of Characters

Every corner or group needs an inner core of dependable, take-charge guys who are always involved and always there, the kind of guys who provide excitement. Well, this group of guys was not them. The only excitement out of this group was strong statements like, "Fuckin' a do," "What are you crazy?", and "The last time you didn't pick me."

Tony Boy always had stories about women he met on Rush Street. He was a few years older than us and had the advantage of stepping out in that area every once in awhile, depending on his cash outlay. We often wondered how he accomplished in the back of a streetcar all the things he bragged about doing with these women.

Ollie was always a part of every story. Every story always ended with ". . . and then there was Ollie."

The Meyers and Skinny Green spent the least amount of time on the corner with several pit stops for minutes at a time. Then the Meyers quit mid-term one summer only to return towards the end of the year with some stories. We didn't believe half the shit he said, but we still listened.

Sonny, the older brother of Lory and the opposite in demeanor, went to the high school that all the other guys made fun of. It was the school for kids with brains. It prepared guys for college and had lousy sports teams. We could kid the school, but never Sonny. And if you did, you would have big problems talking through your ass.

Then there was Joe Boz who one day showed up with a dog bite. Where? On his nose so he said, but then who would bullshit about that? Nobody questioned how he got it, we just said, "Oh yeah, who the fuck is he kidding?" and left it at that.

Mikey was always known for having the biggest stream when taking pees in the alley. At one time the nickname "Champ" was his calling card and he could hit an ant at twenty feet. What an accomplishment that was! If there had been an all city peeing contest, Mikey would certainly have been our entry. Mikey also had a car and was very popular with the guys, until he found out that was the

> "We didn't believe half the shit anyway, but we still listened."

reason why. We would always jump into the back seat to ride around the neighborhood. The front seat was reserved for Fat Frankie most all of the time. So there we were with Mikey and Fat Frankie in the front and six guys in the back of this '49 Chevy. Mikey stopped bringing the car around when he tried to collect gas money and all he got was eight cents and a fuck you.

Chinatown, My Chinatown

Almost once a month, we'd would walk into Chinatown for a dinner of beef fried rice, beef and rice with tomatoes, beef and rice chop no onions, or beef and rice plain. We always ordered a side of toast, too. Why? Nobody knew, we just ordered it. Beef and rice plain with an order of toast. Sounds like shit, but it tasted good.

Chinatown was about one mile from Tooty's Corner, so in the summertime it was a pleasant trip through the neighborhood. Besides that, it provided another opportunity for the guys to play a game called "Screw the Chinaman" or so we thought. Fans of this opportunity were always Richie Cat, Richie Rags, Johnny Boy, myself, and always Fat Frankie. Fats wanted to keep it around four or five guys. We found out much later the reason why.

It sorta of went like this. After everyone had their bellies filled with one of the dishes, each guy would get up and pass the man at the cash register and say,

> "Besides that, it provided another opportunity for the guys to play a game called 'Screw the Chinaman' or so we thought."

"The guy behind me will pick it up," of course referring to the check. Once out the door, each of us would tear down Wentworth Avenue like bats out of hell. The last guy, who was usually the Fat Man, would walk away saying, "See ya," Fats had the nerve to walk, because Fats very seldom ran for anything. The Chinaman would come out of the store screaming to come back and pay.

We always wondered why they never stopped Fat Frankie. It seemed Fats had this thing with some of the Chinese restaurants. Fats would always double back later in the evening and pay the bill. We never found out until many years later when Fats let it be known that this was his thing. What a guy, the Fat Man! It was arranged with the restaurant to go along with this game and all the while we thought we were getting away with something. Oh well, let's toast the Fat Man, wherever he is.

Lory And His Taylor Street Sweetheart

Around 6:30 P.M. on one of those hot summer evenings, I was approaching the corner from the west side of Princeton Avenue, getting ready to cross the street. I noticed out of the corner of my eye a rather large, black car approaching slowly, coming to a stop in front of the corner. Richie Cat was standing in the entrance to Tooty's store, which was closed. I stopped immediately and hid a few feet behind a parked car. I heard the driver of the car say to Cat, "Have you seen Lory?" What I did not notice was that he had a gun concealed from everyone except Cat who struggled to say, "No, I haven't seen him all day." Apparently satisfied with that short reply the car started to slowly move away. I came out from behind the parked car when I saw the black car was not coming back.

Cat was trying to play it cool, but I knew him and we both had to go home and change our shorts. As the story was told on that very morning, Lory had met this broad from Taylor Street (a section on the west side of the city). He hit it off with her and, in Lory's inimical style, promised the girl the moon only to try and give her his *pachook*. She refused and Lory made her walk home. Who knows what she actually told her brothers later. Whatever she said, they got pissed, so their next step was to find Lory. Lory only told the broad he was from Tooty's Corner on 28th and Princeton. It was typical Lory to start shit and leave the corner as a calling card. Naturally, the brothers showed up looking for him.

> "He hit it off with her and, in Lory's inimical style, promised the girl the moon only to try and give her his pachook."

I'm sorta glad he wasn't there. God only knows how it would have played out. I know he would have started something. Everyone always thought Lory could walk through walls. Once, he was involved in a free-for-all in a forest preserve, fighting three guys at the same time. I heard him yell at the top of his lungs, "Goddamn, I love this shit!" He rearranged the faces of all three guys.

As this story turned out, he had already made up with the broad and spent the rest of the day with her, I'm sure making her very happy. She then failed to call off her brothers, who spent most of their day riding around our neighborhood looking for him.

A similar scene played out many years later, but that time it did not work out for Lory. He died as a result of a bullet wound in the street.

The Crooked Chance

In the fifties, there were many guys hanging out in our neighborhood on different corners. Times were different then and so were the corners. There were the 24th Street guys who were wiser, older guys and certainly had the most respect in the neighborhood amongst the corners. The Gophers, another older group, had women hanging out with them. This was a no-no on most all of the other corners. The 29th Street crew, the Aristocrats, were the rowdies and troublemakers. Usually the trouble they started was in other areas, mainly on the south side. They would beat the shit out of several kids in other neighborhoods and tell them they were from the far north side and laugh all the way back to our neighborhood. However, there was a mutual understanding of one another's problems. Yet, there was also great competition between the different blocks and at the same time respect for the individuals on each corner. We never had a lot of money between us except for a few guys and they were not willing to help fund the group. So I better let Sonny and Butchie tell ya'. "Hey Butchie," bellowed Sonny, "we need some money for bats and balls this summer. How do you suppose we get it?" Butchie was big on chance books, especially since he attended St. Rita High School which was known for its chance books. So, of course, he said, "Let's sell chances and raffle something off, but I don't want to run it."

Sonny asked, "Who do we get that's honest?"

Butchie chimed in and said, "The Professor. He'll do it and he's totally honest."

"I don't know if we need all that honesty, but let's ask him. He can't possibly say no."

Butchie said, "Someone has to watch the dollars we collect. Now, what about a prize?"

"The Chain just got a radio for his birthday and he's complaining that it's cheap. Let's buy the radio off him and raffle it."

> "There was a mutual understanding of each other's problems yet there was great competition as well as respect for the individuals on each corner."

"Fuck him! Let's take the radio and owe him later," said Tony Boy who was just standing there listening to all this banter about chances, radios, and money. "We can pay the Chain $5.00 for his radio and raffle off tickets at ten cents a chance or $1.00 a book. Everyone can sell ten books and we'll have enough money to buy plenty of balls and bats." The Chain liked the idea of getting $5.00 so he turned over the radio to the Professor. Everything went as planned and we made over $100.00 on the chances which was certainly enough for the equipment.

Sonny's next idea was to raffle off the radio only among the guys. That way, we'd have the money *and* the radio. Everyone concurred, "Great idea, the only one not eligible to win will be the Chain." There was some opposition displayed by the Chain, but he was quickly vetoed. The Professor ended up winning the radio and sold it back to the Chain for $2.00. Eventually, the Chain sold the radio to someone on 29th Street for $7.00. If you ask me who made out on this deal, I would be unable to tell you. With the money we bought six bats and fifteen baseballs which all disappeared within two months. The only thing I know was that the balls were sent over to Scalise's yard, about one ball for every other game that was played on the four corners. No wonder Joe Bonomo, Scalise's grandson, has this shit-ass grin on his face every time he hears the word "softball."

Spatts Field And The Big Fight

A second favorite hangout was Spatts Field, located several blocks from the corner. Spatts Field was made up of dirt, stones, concrete, and junk. The field sat across the street from Ward School, a rather large building with eighty-four broken windows, on one side alone. Today the field does not exist, but Ward School still does. We used Spatts as a baseball field, a football field, a location for great marble games, and pinners. We played pinners with any soft ball that we could find and threw it against the steps of Ward School. It was also the site of a most famous rumble between Charlie Bolts and Lory. This fight was instigated by Lory, who was complaining he had nothing to do one day. Lory called Charlie a couple of assorted names over a game of pinochle, knowing full well that Bolts always stewed for several hours before he said anything negative to anyone, especially one of the guys.

That afternoon before a group of fifteen to twenty guys playing softball at Spatts, the fix was in as Lory again insulted Bolts (which, by the way, was never done by calling his mother names). "Well enough's enough," Bolts decided and reached out at Lory with a solid right to the head which sparked ten minutes of the finest rumble between two of the neighborhood's toughest guys. Lory had to be hit several times before he even thought of going down and Bolts knew it. Charlie had to wrestle him down, trying to pin him between the concrete. In the process, Charlie ripped his pants which really pissed him off more than the shots he was taking from Lory. As the fight progressed, something eerie

"They both saved face. Nobody lost and nobody won."

happened. Both guys, at exactly the same time, quit. They both threw up their arms and walked away from one another. We all stood around in amazement and only later did we realize that this was good politics within the corner. They both saved face. Nobody lost and nobody won. That night, Bolts and Lory spent several hours bullshitting with one another over everything—except the fight. And none of us ever mentioned it again.

Let's Talk Food. I'm Sorry, I Mean Hamburgers

Let's talk food. This was an evening when the moon was full and everyone on the corner was rumbling about someone or something, until the next subject matter surfaced. Hamburgers. And where to get them at 10:00 P.M. at night?

My man, Yo-Yo, was noted for his eating habits at all hours of the day and night. And of course, Fat Frankie certainly did not want to be known as second best. Then into the ring came Nick the Stick who was as skinny as Fat Frankie was fat.

Competition reigned supreme on the corner, competition over everything. Who could eat more? Fats, Yo-Yo or the Stick. The argument heated up so much that bets were being taken on who could eat the most and, at this late hour, White Castle was the spot for the showdown. Precisely at 10:30 P.M., six carloads of guys descended on the local White Castle on Archer Avenue to find out who had the biggest appetite.

Could it be Fat Frankie who weighed in at around two hundred fifty pounds? Could it be Yo-Yo, noted for eating several jalung sandwiches at one sitting or what about the dark horse, Nick the Stick, known for his shark-eating habits, despite his size? I would really enjoy telling you that Nick the Stick won this food orgy, but after twenty-one sliders he quit with severe stomach cramps. Yo-Yo and Fat Frankie ate away, but ten minutes and five hamburgers later Fats quit at twenty-six saying that his hamburgers were larger than Yo-Yo's. That's why Yo-Yo lives on as "King of All Hamburgers." Yo-Yo ended up glomming down thirty-two—a number that will live in infamy. Yo-Yo won the match and $60.00 in side bets. Also, he did not have to pay for his hamburgers, which really made him happy. That encounter was certainly the talk of the corner the next day and for months to come. To this day it certainly brings a warm smile to Yo-Yo's heart and stomach. Johnny Boy and the Meyers also were big winners on that warm summer evening since they bet Yo-Yo all the way.

> "My man, Yo-Yo, was noted for his eating habits at all hours of the day and night."

Let's Hear It For Religion And Big Dollars

Sunday morning was a time for church for most guys on the corner thanks to our moms' insistence. However, the Chain turned church time into a financial windfall for himself.

The Chain received this nickname because of the over zealous way he handled a bicycle chain when it was not attached to a bike. One summer afternoon he was attacked by several guys outside the neighborhood. And I'm sure they were surprised when he did a number on their heads with the bicycle chain he was carrying in the small briefcase he used to stroll around with. Nevertheless, he was picked by the good nuns to walk around the church during collection times for two masses each Sunday morning. Now picture this, there was a balcony and a first floor. To get to the balcony you had to go up a small passageway climbing up a flight of stairs.That's where the Chain made his weekly collection run. As he made his way up and down the stairs, the loose bills from the collection plate somehow wandered their way into the Chain's pockets. He always said that the church was good to him and rewarded him very well for his time. He made around $25.00 to $50.00 per week and that kept him connected for shows, clothes, and sandwiches.

"And I'm sure they were surprised when he did a number on their heads with the bicycle chain he was carrying in the small briefcase he used to stroll around with."

When he had to surrender this golden opportunity, the Chain tried to no avail to bribe the new kid. After this, he was not a happy camper. But what the hell, it was good time while it lasted.

The Great Wall Caper And Facabruno

Playing ball on the corner was what we called "four corners." We used the manhole covers located on each tip of the corner near the curb as bases. These covers took care of all the rainwater on the street, letting it flow into the city's sewer system. For us, they were the perfect stationary bases. The batter's box was the cover nearest the corner and the pitcher's mound was in the middle of the street. Play was always interrupted by passing cars and occasional dogs which found it necessary to run after the balls that were hit onto Princeton and 28th Street. You see, Princeton was in left field and 28th Street was in right. Center field housed the infamous Scalise yard. That was the dead zone, hitting it there meant the game was over. We had no center field, but I roamed in left and

Bobby D. did the same in right. Charlie Bolts was an automatic out at third base and Petey Boy played short. The Rags was at second and the very stylish Nick the Stick at first. The Stick was noted for his big hands and caught everything that was sent to him. As long as the Stick touched it, he caught it. Fat Frankie was the catcher and Richie Cat pitched because neither one liked to run. What a winning combination!

Late one summer evening, Norman Bates and Nick the Stick decided to retrieve some of the balls that they knew were still in Old Man Scalise's yard. You could not see into the yard because of the tree branches and old plants which decorated the old wire fence that surrounded it. You could not see in, nor could the old man see out. But Bates and the Stick were certain that there had to be balls somewhere in the yard. With the help of a full moon, they scaled the fence around midnight and were not on the ground longer than five minutes when the Stick said, "Look in the corner, there must be twenty-five balls."

The balls were placed in neat piles and they had our names written all over them.

All of a sudden, the guys on the other side saw balls flying over the fence. Big, little, new, old, and all colors. It looked like it was snowing the way Bates and the Stick were sending them over.

All the guys celebrated that night, but the following morning Old Man Scalise was in Tooty's store swearing and carrying on about the missing balls. "Some of the guys that hang on this corner were in my yard last night. What are you going to do about it?" asked Scalise.

Tooty said, "Nothing. I don't know anything about it. Besides that, what are you talking about? Those are not your baseballs anyway. You keep them when they go over the fence. I'm sorta glad they got them if that's what happened."

"Well, I'm going to get myself a dog that will bite their asses if they ever try that again," Old Man Scalise yelled and stormed out of the store.

The following morning while sitting in front of his store drinking his morning coffee, Tooty told Tony Boy and Ollie about his conversation. Tooty would, from time to time, bullshit with the guys when he was not harassing his customers. Tooty was never known for his personality or his patience.

Ollie came up with a fantastic idea, "Let's sell, or better yet, give the old man his wish. My cousin has this dog who is afraid of his own shadow, but happens to do a great imitation of a guard dog. He used to be mine until I gave him to my cousin last summer because my mother did not want to put up with him any longer. The old man will think he's got a winner and we can come and go with the dog being on our side. The dog's name is Facabruno." Everyone thought the idea was great. Now Tooty had to sell the idea to Scalise, and that he did.

The following day after the old man left his house to do his daily chores, we hit a few balls into the yard to see what Facabruno would do. We waited until evening to retrieve our balls from the yard and to check in with Facabruno. We never went over the wall that night, but the following morning Scalise was in Tooty's store. This time he was informing Tooty of the dog's demise. It seems the dog ate not only the three balls we hit over the fence, but several others he found. It was the end of the balls and the dog.

We sorta felt guilty every time we hit a ball over the fence, even though that did not stop us from doing it. But, we did toast Facabruno whenever it happened and that dog will go down in history in some strange way as a member of Tooty's Corner.

Richie Cat And The Rock

Richie Cat had the winning round in the Rocky Marciano versus Jersey Joe Wolcott fight at the Chicago Stadium. Tickets were picked by Cat and fifteen other guys who bet $100.00 each to get into the corner's lottery regarding this championship heavyweight fight. Cat picked the very first round. "What a shit round," he thought and then proceeded to try and get rid of the ticket all day. "I'll sell this round for $50.00—half of what I paid for it," exclaimed Cat. He wanted to at least accummulate a fraction of the cost. Nick the Stick and Ollie said they wouldn't buy that ticket for $25.00. Tony Boy told Cat that he would buy the ticket out of the kindness of his heart *and* pocketbook for $10.00. Cat told him where he could put the $10.00. Cat could not get rid of that ticket to save his life.

At 9:00 P.M., the fight started. The fight was blacked out in Chicago because it was a sellout in the stadium at the last hour. We congregated around the radio which blared from Tooty's store. He decided to stay open until 10:00 P.M. that evening since there were so many guys on the corner. Side bets were ringing up loud and clear. I don't think I need to tell you what happened. The radio blared, "Marciano, a right to the head. Marciano, a left to the body. Marciano, another right to the head and Wolcott is down." One minute and twenty-five seconds into the first round Marciano knocked out Wolcott. Wolcott wasn't the only one stunned; so was Cat. All of a sudden the Cat became the greatest sports bettor of all time, bragging how he knew all along that the Rock would knock out Jersey Joe in the first round.

With more money than he ever had in his life, he was the provider of junk food for everyone who just happened to stop by the corner that eventful summer evening.

> "One minute and twenty-five seconds into the first round Marciano knocked out Wolcott."

Kenny And Don't Know

The corner provided escape for most of the guys that spent any time there. We had one another to complain to. We listened to each other and offered advice regarding right and wrong. We had all the answers we needed and we had a lot of questions to ask. Most of the time neither the questions nor the answers made any sense, but we were comfortable in asking all the same. We certainly were not going to ask our parents or teachers about sex and things of that sort. Instead, we had Nick the Stick to tell us all about his relationships with women and after that we knew all there was to know about sex.

Like the night one of the broads from the other side of the viaduct claimed she had gotten pregnant by Skinny Green. Skinny was visibly upset and came to the corner

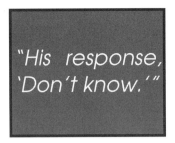

"*His response, 'Don't know.'*"

for some sound advice. The Molly said, "Fuck her! Don't pay her any attention." The Boz followed with, "We all know you don't even know how to use it, so don't worry about anything." All this sound advice made Skinny feel very comfortable about the unfortunate situation. He thanked God that he had the corner guys.

Kenny was responsible for telling us about his experiences with his parents which showed us how to handle or at least attempt to deal with ours. Kenny's mother used to ask him, "Where are you going?" His response, "Don't know."

"When are you coming home?" His response, "Don't know."

"Who are you seeing?" His response, you guessed it, "Don't know."

Kenny said his "don't know" three times per day, every day for two years which added up to over two thousand times. Kenny bought a Mother's Day card and signed it, "Don't know." He mailed the card and when his mother got the card, she told Kenny that she must have gotten this card by mistake and it was a shame that the mother of "Don't Know" wasn't going to get one.

Jimmy C. And His Trained Coins

I don't think anyone understood how we came to be on the corner. For me, it was like a private island where I could go to feel important and safe. I always enjoyed coming to the corner for a full day of activities like playing cards, baseball, bullshiting, and pitching pennies, nickels, dimes, or quarters. When it came to pitching coins, the best of the best was Jimmy C. He always had change in his pockets.

He used to knock over gum ball machines for change. If you needed change, forget the store, just see Jimmy C. He always wanted to pitch dimes or quarters and when he won after each toss, he would race to the line to pick up the coins. If you wanted to put a coin on a line, get Jimmy C. He could do it with his eyes closed.

I liked to watch him pitch coins for side money. I'd bet a dollar on the side and then pitch three quarters, closest to the line wins. He spent hours finding suckers for this and would walk away with two pockets of change. At the end of the day he would see Tooty to change his coins for bills. This played out with Jimmy every day for three to four months. He accumulated enough money to keep him going all winter long.

One day a salesman was visiting Tooty and he was convinced by the greatest bull shitters in the neighborhood, Joe Boz and Nick the Stick, to take on Jimmy C. in a quarter game of pitching coins. This guy thought he was pretty good, especially when he noticed Jimmy C., who noticed him watching, not being able to hit the line with a softball.

The sales guy made the ultimate mistake by saying, "Well, Jimmy, would you like to pitch some quarters?" These were magic words to Jimmy C. and he even had his own personal cheerleaders with the Boz and the Stick watching. One hour later, Jimmy C. had enough coins in his pocket to walk with a limp. As the sales guy left the corner, Jimmy C. had another victim in his pocket along with about $35.00 in quarters.

"Hey Jimmy C. you got change for a buck?" anyone would ask.

"What are you, fucking nuts? Of course I do. You want to pitch for it?"

Let's Hear It For Tooty

The store really hasn't changed much over the years, in fact, come to think of it, neither has Tooty. As you walk in for the first time you notice back in the rear of the store stood a desk, a phone, a meat counter, and a walk-in cooler. The cooler was where Tooty conducted business. The grocery store has been at 28th and Princeton forever. In fact, when my father was a kid he worked for Tooty's old man. Tooty, an avid White Sox fan, could be heard for blocks away cheering for those "fucking White Sox."

Few of us were ever allowed to hang in the store. Outside was okay, but inside was not okay. You had to be a favorite of Tooty's to achieve inside privileges. The group with those credentials consisted of Charlie Bolts, Richie Cat, Johnny Boy, the Professor, and me. Why us? I always thought it was because our mothers shopped in the store at one time or another and Tooty did not want to piss them off. So we became part of the scenery. We also made a great audience for the cast of characters that came in and out of the store from time to time. There was Caesar, the talking Italian cowboy; Rails, the bread man (a favorite of Tooty's); and Curly, the millionaire elevator repair guy, who smoked around eighty cigarettes a day because he owned stock in Liggitt & Meyers. He always said, "Need to keep the stock up, boys. Buy those cigarettes."

When these characters moved in and out of the store, we became privy to their conversations. We were a lot younger and very impressionable, but not a day went by that we were not imitating some of the shit those guys were doing. We then brought that nonsense outside to the corner to share with the rest of the guys.

> *"To this day 39 years later, if you stop by and say hello to Tooty, the atmosphere is still the same."*

To this day, thirty-nine years later, if you stop by and say hello to Tooty (who is still there) the atmosphere is the same. The same elements exist: telephone, desk, cooler, and meat counter and as always—Tooty. Now there's no more hanging on the corner; the guys from my generation are gone. We were the last and the best. Tooty wouldn't have had it any other way. Just ask him.

The Miles And The Unfortunate Post

One lazy Sunday afternoon, I decided that it was time to borrow my father's car for a leisurely drive around the neighborhood. Richie Rags and Nap thought this would be great and of course further encouraged me, even though my father had said no to repeated requests to use the vehicle. My father's car was in the garage since he didn't use it on a day-to-day basis. If anything, the vehicle was used maybe only once a month. We thought my old man was old, but he was probably only in his forties at the time. He was quite a golfer and spent many hours on the course. We always wondered how he got there since the car was always in the garage.

Naps and Rags jumped into the vehicle with the garage door up and me behind the wheel. As I was making the short turn from the garage into the alley, we all heard a loud crunch. The fender on the passenger side was gone. "Nice going," said Richie Rags. "Where the fuck did you learn how to drive? In Tooty's store?" Naps and Rags decided that the ride was over and did not want to deal with me or my old man, so they left the vehicle and stood around the car giving me encouraging words like, "What an asshole. You told us you could drive."

I had two choices as I saw it. Either forget to tell my father that there was damage to the vehicle or have the car repaired before he saw the bang up job I had done.

Naps said the total damage was in the neighborhood of $500.00. I asked, "How do you know? Are you in the body shop business?"

> "'Nice going,' said Richie Rags. 'Where the fuck did you learn how to drive? In Tooty's store?'"

"No," said Naps, "I got a feel." Well, that feel made me decide that no way, no how was I going to tell my old man. I backed the car into the garage and swore everyone to secrecy. Several months later my father asked if I knew anything about the damage to the car. If my father found out that I had anything to do with this and did not tell him, he would have twisted my head and arms around my neck. I'd have had to learn how to drive with my feet. Naturally I said, "No way, Pop. Why? Something wrong?"

The two jokers and I kept our word and our secret for thirty-nine years. Of course, my father is long gone, having died never knowing how the car was damaged.

By the way, at the reunion, the topic resurfaced and the actual repairs cost $523.00. Everyone said, "Thatta way Nap. They all said you didn't know what the hell you were talking about."

Ironically, I was the last guy from the corner to own my own car and the first guy from the corner to leave and move on to other avenues and neighborhoods.

Lory And Fat Frankie's Dilemma In The Loop

The 15 September 1955 was a day that two guys from the corner would have liked to forget. Lory and Fat Frankie decided, since it was raining, it would be a good time to go downtown to roam and work the stores. Both Lory and Frankie jumped on the Wentworth Avenue streetcar and dodged the conductor so they did not have to pay the fare, which was really a Lory thing. Beating the CTA was a great score for him. He would say, "Beating the system, that's what it's all about." Fat Frankie would create a disturbance and Lory would file back into the crowd that was getting on or off the streetcar. Most of the time the conductor, because he didn't want to deal with Frankie, would let him on so both Lory and Frankie did not have to pay.

Lory and Frankie decided that Madison Street would be a great starting point because you could go in any direction and all the stores were at their beck and call. Fields and Carson's were all there. Fats and Lory would only shop at the better stores downtown. To see Lory and Frankie work a store was a piece of work. They needed shirts, they got shirts. They needed shoes, they got shoes. We would always wonder how. Well, we really knew deep down how they always looked good, but nobody asked. Everyone always kept quiet when you were wondering about Lory and Fat Frankie's escapades. As they were working the stores on that fateful day, Fat Frankie looked up from doing what he did best, which was sorting out the best merchandise he wanted to keep at Marshall Fields. Then, as Lory looked up, he noticed that there were other people watching Frankie while he was sorting his favorite silk ties. Frankie whispered to Lory in a low voice, "I don't like the look of this situation. Let's get the fuck out of here and quickly." Lory did not question Fats because by this time he knew something was going down and he didn't like it either. Of course, they both looked very guilty with their brand new shoes and shirts as they walked quickly through the suits that surely would have been next on their hit list. When they neared the store's exit, several guys surrounded the two and said, "Keep walking, but slowly, and keep your eyes straight ahead." Lory and Frankie disregarded their commands. "Fuck you guys!" said Frankie in a loud voice. Lory said, "Second the motion, assholes." These two really knew how to make friends fast.

Two cars were waiting at the curb. Frankie was shuttled into one and Lory in the other. Four guys each accompanied them into the car, but they remained silent about who they were and where they were going. No words were exchanged as the cars sped down Wabash going south towards Archer Avenue. Both Frankie and Lory noticed that these cars were going back into the neighborhood. Total confusion then set in. Frankie asked, "What the hell is going on? This is my neighborhood."

The cars backed into an alley on 24th Street and both Frankie and Lory were brought into a room with Charlie P. and Paul the Envelope. They both stood in a corner talking to each another. These were the local "patrons" in charge of keeping harmony within the neighborhood. They were great guys if you wanted to bullshit about the Bears or Cardinals; bad guys if you created problems for them in their neighborhood. No bricks had to fall on the

> *"No words were exchanged as the cars sped down Wabash going south towards Archer Avenue."*

guys' heads to realize that this conversation would be about their morning at the downtown stores.

Charlie P. looked at Frankie and Lory directly which made the guys just a little bit nervous. He addressed them as "sweethearts." Everything was "sweetheart" with Charlie P. whose reputation was synonymous with heads rolling in the streets. Only when someone needed attention did Charlie P. get involved. Only when someone started some shit did Charlie P. get involved. Paul the Envelope was there for window dressing and to compliment and certainly enforce whatever Charlie P. said.

Charlie said, "You fuckin' guys will never learn. You go downtown starting shit and bring it back into the neighborhood. Then we have to deal with it."

Lory, being the smartass, said, "The only thing we're bringing back today is one shirt and one pair of shoes."

Charlie retorted, "Listen shithead no more fucking around downtown. You guys are lucky you're getting a second chance, which is rare around here."

The meeting took all of five minutes and Frankie and Lory were left to walk back to the corner which was a mile away. As they approached, Petey and Joe Boz asked, "Where the hell are you guys coming from? You look all upset about something."

Not a good thing to say. All they got as a reply was, "Fuck you, don't ask any questions, jerk." There was no way Frankie or Lory would tell anyone what had happened. All they had in the back of their minds was getting even. They figured that the 24th Street guys had received a phone call from downtown that someone from Tooty's Corner was stealing in the Loop and that it needed to be stopped.

Frankie and Lory both realized that stepping on the toes of the guys on 24th Street was risky and there had to be ramifications. This was why they didn't believe Charlie P. and the Envelope when they said, "Just get the hell out of here and please stop." They also knew that other people were involved, so they understood the gravity of the situation.

Both Frankie and Lory were pissed. They were embarrassed about how they were ushered out of the store. That scene tarnished their reputation within the neighborhood and corner. They both decided to let it rest for the time being and go about their normal routine.

It was a hot morning when the phone rang at Fat Frankie's house. On the line was Rocco, who was a runner for a lot of guys from 24th Street. He said in a excited voice, "Fats, we need to meet with Lory as soon as possible. What are you doing this afternoon?" Fats got a little nervous because he had never received a phone call from Rocco, and his bones were telling him that this had something to do with the shit downtown. When Fats told Lory of the proposed meeting, Lory went out of his mind. "What are they, fucking nuts? I'll meet them on my terms, not theirs. Screw them, Fats. Let's call Rocco and tell him so." Fats knew that would only compound the problem. To calm Lory down Fats said, "I'll call Rocco and get him to meet on the corner at 3:00 P.M. and nowhere else." Fats was reluctant to meet anywhere except in the open regarding this matter. Lory wasn't thinking. He just wanted to get this finished and did not want to bow down or listen to what anyone had to say about it. It was up to Fats to make peace.

Fats was getting nervous about the situation and brought in several guys for a consultation. Unknown to Lory, Fats called in Richie Rags and the Cat. Although Fats was nervous, his mischievous mind was starting to work. He had Lory on his side and he sorta liked the pending intrigue with 24th Street.

Richie Rags and Richie Cat were easy. "Apologize to those guys. Listen to what they have to say and do it. Life is good. Why do you want to fuck with it." They also told Fats they would not say anything to anyone about it. Which meant that by noon everyone on the corner knew about the episode downtown and the meeting. This was a huge mistake. Fats knew that saying tell no one meant they would tell everyone. At 11:30 that morning, after Fats got off the phone with Rocco, the meeting was set up for Spatts Field where Fats felt comfortable. Unknown to Lory, Fats wanted everyone from the corner to be there playing ball or just hanging around.

"This is great," Fats told himself. "Whoever shows from 24th will have to contend not only with Lory, but everyone from the corner." Naturally the guys received ten different stories by noon on what was going down, but they all agreed to be there anyway. Fats sat down with a jalung sandwich at Tooty's and held court on the upcoming events. He was really getting into some amazing stories on what really went down with the 24th street crew in the Loop. Most of it was bullshit. You would have thought that Capone had been talking to Fats and Lory.

In the meantime, Lory was at home talking to Sonny about the upcoming meeting and Sonny was also trying to calm down Lory, who got more pissed every time he opened his mouth. When Sonny and Lory got to the corner around 12:30 P.M. they found out that everyone knew about the meeting. Lory went ballistic again. Compared to Fat Frankie, Lory didn't talk much. Frankie, on the other hand, was selling the idea to everyone. "Listen Fats, you big asshole, what the hell are you doing? I'm not going to Spatts Field and no one is coming with us. I still haven't made up my mind on whether I want to meet with any jerk-off from 24th Street or not. You're turning this into a circus. Call Rocco back and explain to him—better yet—find out what he wants and who is attending this so-called meeting. I want to know who is going to be there and what we are going to talk about. I'm not going to end up in the trunk of some car for some petty bullshit downtown. Besides, why is Rocco involved anyway? Get on this right away so I can calm down, you big clown. Man you piss me off." Sonny reminded Lory to play it cool and stay out of trouble by not listening to Frankie or anyone else. Telling that to Lory was like talking to the man in the moon.

When Lory said anything he meant it. So Frankie tried to call Rocco back to inform him of Lory's decision but got no answer. Frankie suspected that since it was after twelve, Rocco was already running around. This upset Frankie because he didn't want to deal with 24th Street and he certainly didn't want to deal with Lory. The conversations on the corner that day were mixed and certainly confusing about what the hell was going on. The guys did not want to upset the people from 24th Street and they didn't want to upset anybody on any corner in the neighborhood.

The time for the meeting was rapidly approaching. The guys were filtering out to Spatts Field with Fat Frankie leading the parade. Lory, who lived right down the street from Spatts, was home laying on the floor watching the ballgame as if he had no cares in the world. Sonny wanted to get to Spatts early, so he was actually the first one there waiting for everyone else. Because of the nagging of Sonny, Fat Frankie, and all the guys, Lory relented and went along with everyone else. At exactly 3:00 P.M., as everyone was milling around, they spotted a new, red Mercury Marquis coming slowly down Shields Avenue with Rocco sitting in the driver's seat. "Hey Rocco, looking strong," was the cry from most of the envious guys milling around his car. Rocco came to a stop in front of where the guys were standing.

Rocco motioned to Fat Frankie and Lory to get into the car for a short drive up the street. Fats got in but Lory said, "Fuck you! What do you want? Just tell me here. We don't need to ride anywhere." Rocco then opened the door and walked towards Lory and said in a whisper, "Okay, okay, the only message I have for you is an apology for the incident downtown and the way it was handled. We know your opportunities will not be downtown any longer, as it should be. We're sorry again for any inconvenience this has created."

Lory was stunned and so was Fats who picked up the end of the conversation. Rocco proceeded to get back into his car and took off with all the guys still looking in amazement at the car and at Lory who also just stood there.

Weeks later everyone found out what really happened. It seemed that Tooty got wind of something major going down between two of his guys on the corner and 24th Street. Then the downtown incident happened. Tooty appealed to Big Ferdi, the boss of all bosses, who in turn told Charlie P. and the Envelope to act like humans and leave it alone. You see, Big Ferdi was the original guy to receive the phone call from the stores about Fat and Lory. Because of Tooty's stature in the neighborhood, 24th Street backed off. Thank you, Tooty. That was the day we all really found out we were his guys.

The Big Night—First And Last Of Its Kind For Tooty's Guys

As we piled into our cars to drive to the Doubletree for an evening we would never forget, it seemed like old times. We had always piled into each other's cars whenever one of the guys needed help or just to drive around the neighborhood to keep it safe. A distress call always pulled us together.

Pulling up to the hotel and seeing the sign in the lobby that welcomed us was special. This was our event. It was like vindication in a strange sort of a way. We had come together after being apart for thirty-nine years. We had all managed to congregate in one spot again. I saw Tooty with his eyes full of tears and his chest swollen with pride. These were his guys, the guys he never kicked off his corner, the nights he put up with swearing,

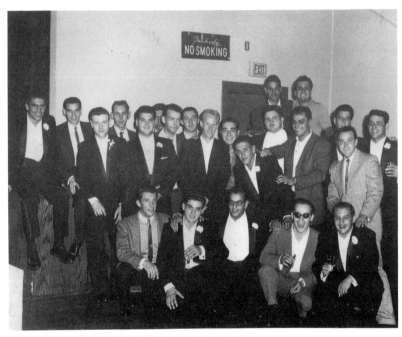

A night out for the guys
1960

baseball, arguments, and whatever else came his way. He stood in front of everyone that evening saying with pride, "You guys have made my day, my evening, and the memories will be with me until the day I die. Thank you for that." I heard Yo-Yo say, "Thatta way Tooty." And I saw it

> "I have my own personal and special memories about Lory, Fats, Skinny Green, and Bobby D."

in Sonny's eyes, "Man, Lory, you should have been here, too." Rags did not have to say anything. I saw it in his face. I also saw Ollie and Kenny hug. Tony Boy and the Professor talked again about the nonsense that took place amongst everyone. I listened to Naps talk about the money he collected from the Professor and me every morning before going to school in his fine car. Ten cents a ride to St. Rita High School and ten cents coming back.

Molly recounted his motor scooter days and told a story about running down Skinny Green one evening with Molly yelling at him to go put on some weight, so he could be seen. The Chain and Norman Bates tried to start up a dice game that night with Butchie, while Johnny Boy and Nick the Stick wisecracked that it would be a miracle if that took place. We went around the table at dinner and recounted the days which, as the Meyers put it, were our most happy and carefree. Mikey and Jimmy Boy gave him some shit about him being lucky to have the opportunity just to hang on the corner with the guys.

I have my own personal and special memories about Lory, Fats, Skinny Green, and Bobby D.

One evening, I wanted to see if I was up to the task of sparring with Lory one-on-one. Lory did a number on my head just fooling around. I came to the realization that he was truly our number one tough guy.

Fat Frankie was related to me in some distant way, fourteenth cousin removed or something like that. He and I had an invisible bond. He was truly a crowd favorite. He goofed around with everyone and pushed each person's patience, but then bailed out with some sort of joke or funny story. Everyone loved him for his stupid, impish ways.

I hate to admit it, but Skinny Green's clarinet and my accordion played beautiful music together down in my basement. Beautiful music, we always thought, but we played only one song titled "I Get Ideas." If Skinny was alive, we'd have laughed for hours remembering that. He is probably playing that song wherever he is right now.

Bobby D. and I went to college together. He went for his football abilities and I went for basketball. In college, all the women wanted him, not his football abilities. He was a really good looking kid with great body strength. Seeing him in a casket several years ago took all the strength I could muster. Cancer. What a waste. It did a real heavy number on his body and mind.

Bona mane Lory, Fat Frankie, Skinny Green, and Bobby D. They were remembered with love that evening at the dinner. *Bona mane,* meaning "gone and dead."

And to Rags and Yo-Yo my fine friends, who one afternoon in June said, "Lets go for it! A reunion will be a once in a lifetime opportunity and we can do it." And you know what? We did.

Tooty's checks out

BY JIM RITTER

STAFF REPORTER

Tooty's, a corner grocery on the Near South Side, quietly went out of business Sunday after three generations and 84 years.

Tooty's couldn't match the large selection and low prices of chain supermarkets. Nor was Tooty's as bright and clean as Jewel and Dominick's.

But owner Salvatore "Tooty" Quattrocki gave customers from China-town and Bridgeport something perhaps more valuable: they type of personalized service that is disappearing as mom-and-pop grocery stores go out of business.

Tooty would greet customers by their first names. He'd banter about his beloved White Sox and that other team from the North Side. He'd ask if you wanted a loaf of fresh bread, or some of his wife Frances' homemade Italian sausage.

There was no room for shopping carts in the cramped store at 28th and Princeton. No need, for that matter. The groceries were stacked behind the counter, and Tooty would fetch the milk, Wheaties and canned peaches. He also delivered groceries to shut-ins.

Short of cash? Tooty would extend credit, at no interest. He was a good judge of character. Only five customers failed to pay him back— one deadbeat for every decade Tooty ran the store.

And no one ever robbed him.

"It's like the center of the neighborhood," said longtime customer Dan Devine, who dropped by Sunday to say goodbye and to buy the last piece of sausage. "They're going to be missed."

Tooty's grandfather, Salvatore Quattroki, came to Chicago from Sicily. He peddled fruit, saved money and opened the store in 1914. Around 1922, mob thugs came by, demading protection money. Salvatore refused, but the stress led to a nervous breaksown. So Tooty's father, Joseph, took over.

Tooty began working in the store after school at age 10. He would wait on customers and help butcher chickens in the basement.

After high school and a stint in the Marines, Tooty thought about entering the insurance business or going to Notre Dame. But the day after Tooty got home from the Marines, his father got sick.

Tooty has been behind the counter ever since. He worked 6 a.m. to 7 p.m. six days a week, and five hours on Sundays.

Tooty, 70, has missed just one day due to illness. He remains in good health, but Frances had an operation last year, and their doctor insisted they retire. Sons Joe and Jimmy don't want to replace their father behind the counter.

"The money wasn't any good, and the hours stink," Jimmy said.

Tooty and Frances will continue living upstairs. They may convert the first floor to an apartment. Even if they don't, another family grocery will become a neighborhood memory.

As chain supermarkets grow ever larger, their buying power increases. This translates into low prices that mom-and-pops can't hope to match.

Between 1987 and 1997, the number of small grocery stores in the United States declined by 43 percent, to 39,970, the Food Marketing Institute said.

Greg Gattuso, retail editor of Supermarket News, compares the decline of the mom-and-pop grocery store to the death of the Sears catalog.

"It was an American institution for a long time," Gattuso said. "That kind of service is disappearing."